BLUES FOR FLUTE

Wise Publications
London/New York/Paris/Sydney/Copenhagen/Madrid

Exclusive Distributors:
Music Sales Limited
8/9 Frith Street,
London W1V 5TZ, England.

Music Sales Pty Limited
120 Rothschild Avenue,
Rosebery, NSW 2018,
Australia.

Order No. AM952017
ISBN 0-7119-7178-1
This book © Copyright 1998 by Wise Publications

Compiled by Peter Evans
Music arranged by Jack Long
Music processed by Enigma Music Production Services
Cover design by Chloë Alexander
Printed in the United Kingdom by
Page Bros, Norwich.

Your Guarantee of Quality
As publishers, we strive to produce every book to the highest
commercial standards.
The music has been freshly engraved and the book has been
carefully designed to minimise awkward page turns and to
make playing from it a real pleasure.
Particular care has been given to specifying acid-free, neutral-
sized paper made from pulps which have not been elemental
chlorine bleached. This pulp is from farmed sustainable forests
and was produced with special regard for the environment.
Throughout, the printing and binding have been planned to
ensure a sturdy, attractive publication which should give years
of enjoyment.
If your copy fails to meet our high standards, please inform us
and we will gladly replace it.

Music Sales' complete catalogue describes thousands of titles
and is available in full colour sections by subject, direct from
Music Sales Limited. Please state your areas of interest and
send a cheque/postal order for £1.50 for postage to:
Music Sales Limited, Newmarket Road, Bury St. Edmunds,
Suffolk IP33 3YB.

Fingering Guide

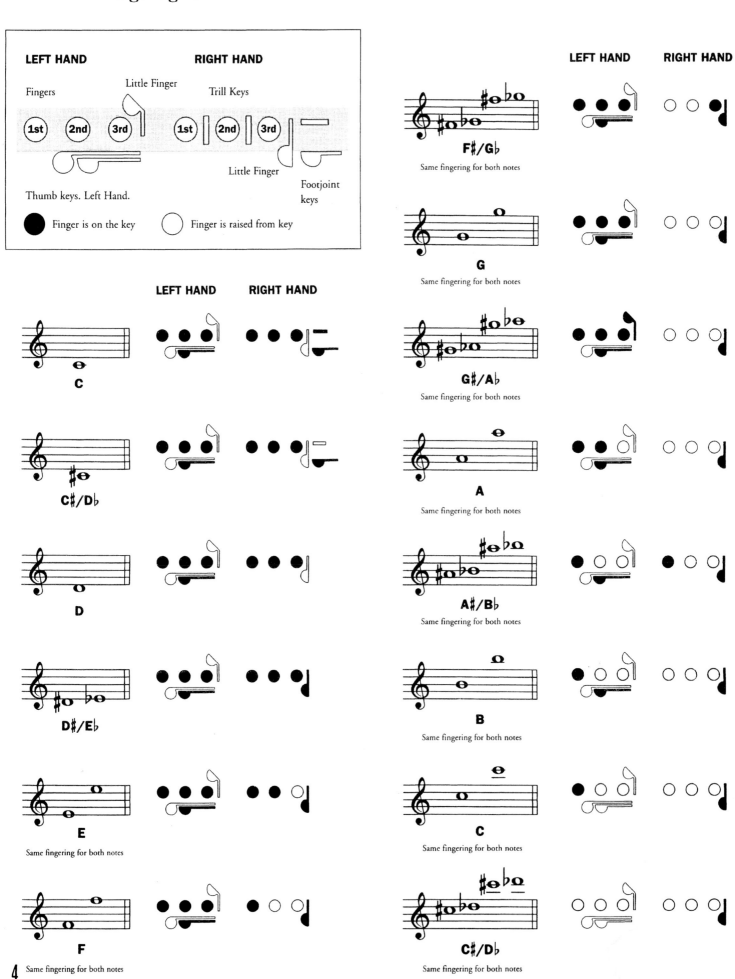

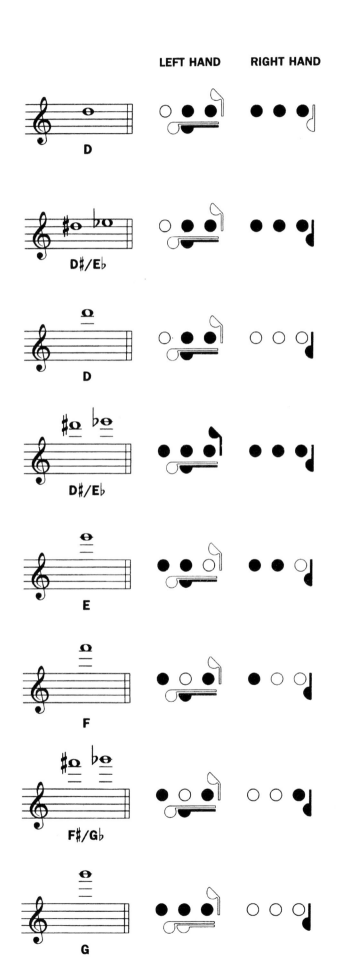

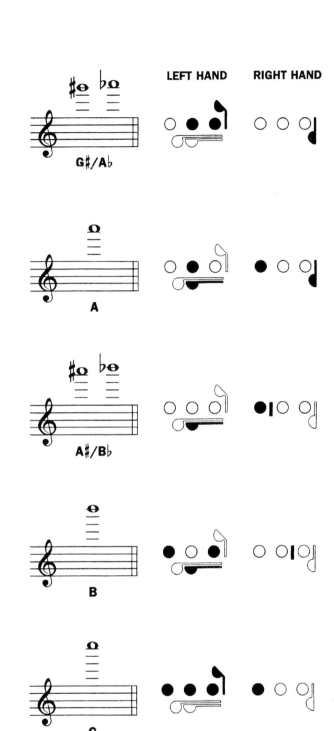

Alright, Okay, You Win

Words & Music by Sid Wyche & Mayme Watts

Medium swing

7

Basin Street Blues

Words & Music by Spencer Williams

8

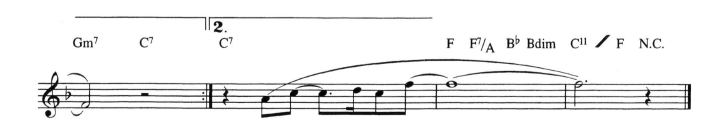

Black Coffee

Words & Music by Paul Francis Webster & Sonny Burke

Medium slow

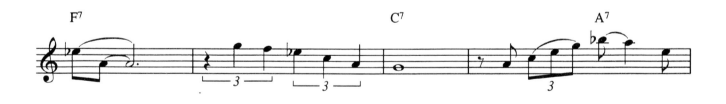

Blues Around My Bed

Words & Music by Spencer Williams

Blues My Naughty Sweetie Gives To Me

Words & Music by Arthur N. Swanstrom, Charles R. McGarron & Carey Morgan

Medium fast

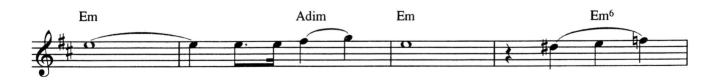

Blues Stay Away From Me

Words & Music by Wayne Raney, Henry Glover, Alton Delmore & Rabon Delmore

Blue Monk

By Thelonious Monk

Medium tempo

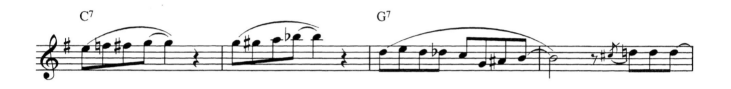

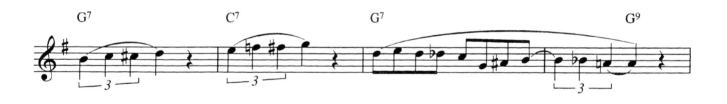

17

Body And Soul

Music by John Green ▮ Lyrics by Frank Eyton, Edward Heyman & Robert Sour

Buddy Bolden's Blues

By Ferdinand 'Jelly Roll' Morton

Medium swing

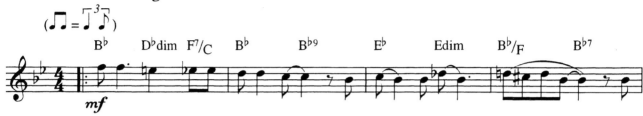

19

But Beautiful

Words by Johnny Burke ▮ Music by Jimmy Van Heusen

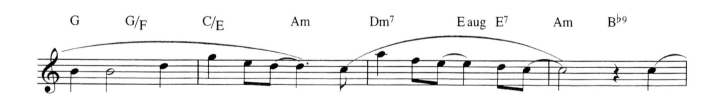

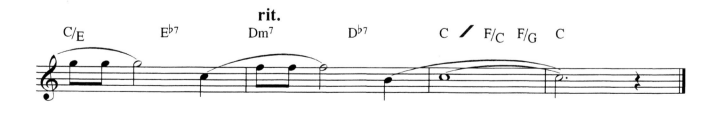

21

Come Sunday

By Duke Ellington

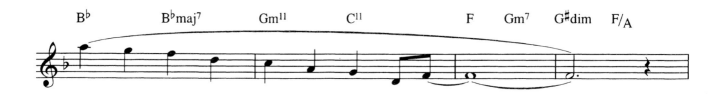

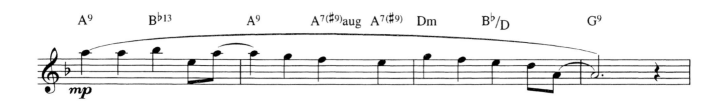

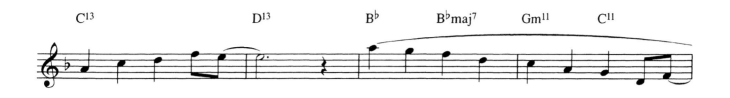

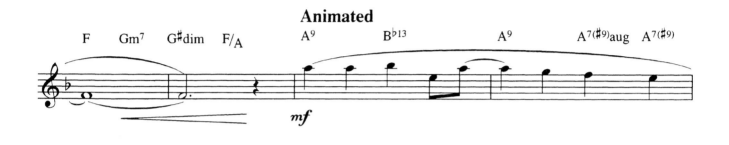

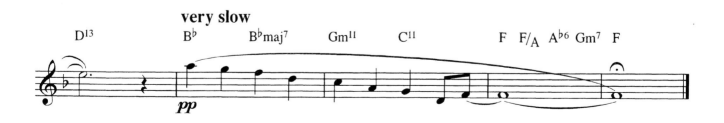

Cotton Tail

By Duke Ellington

Medium fast

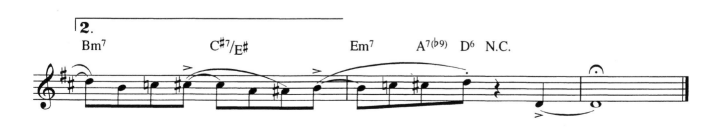

Canal Street Blues

By Joe 'King' Oliver

Medium tempo

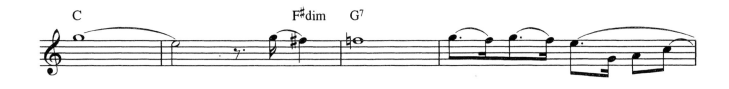

Do Nothin' Till You Hear From Me

Words & Music by Duke Ellington & Bob Russell

Don't Blame Me

Words & Music by Jimmy McHugh & Dorothy Fields

Fever

Words & Music by John Davenport & Eddie Cooley

Medium swing

Get On Board, Little Children

Words & Music by Don Raye & Gene de Paul

Fast 'Gospel' swing

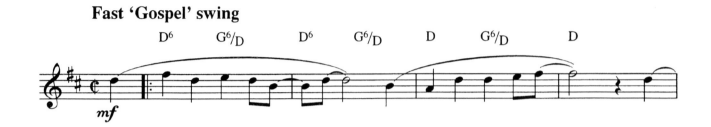

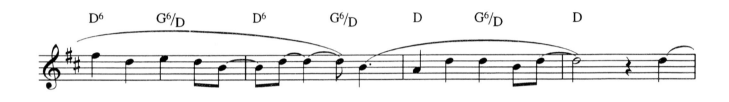

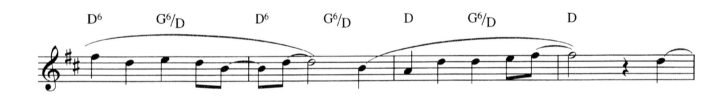

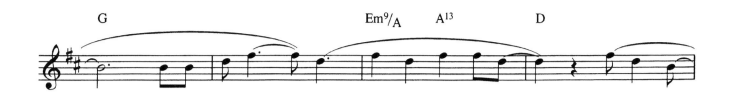

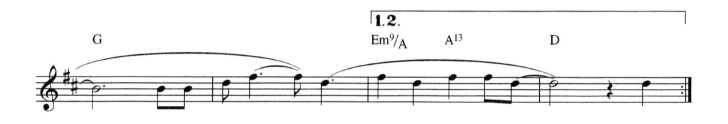

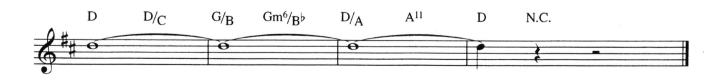

Hard Hearted Hannah

Words & Music by Jack Yellen, Milton Ager, Bob Bigelow & Charles Bates

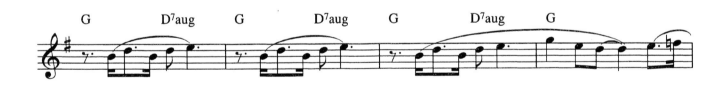

Harlem Nocturne

Music by Earle Hagen ▪ Words by Dick Rogers

Slow

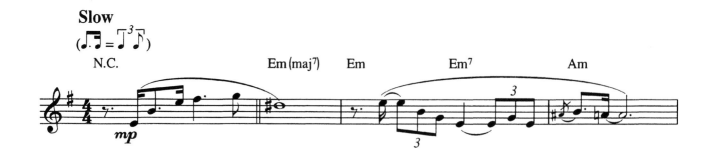

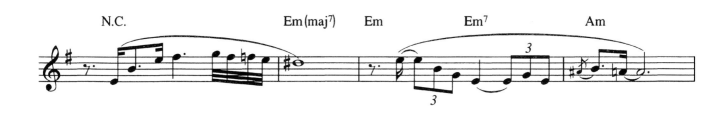

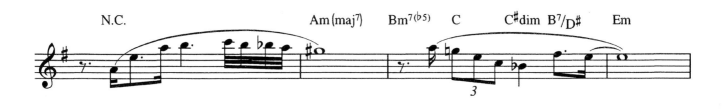

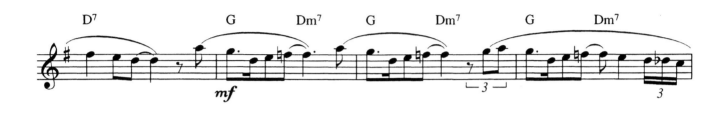

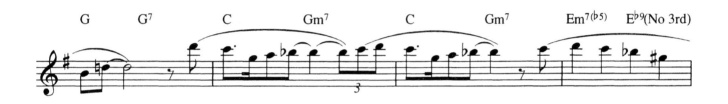

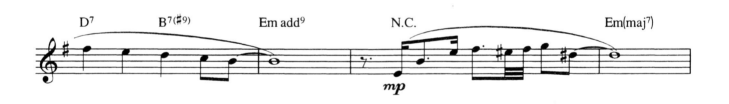

Hand Me Down Love

Words & Music by Duke Ellington & Carl Sigman

If I Had You

Words & Music by Ted Shapiro, Jimmy Campbell & Reg Connelly

I Ain't Got Nobody (And There's Nobody Cares For Me)

Words & Music by Roger Graham & Spencer Williams

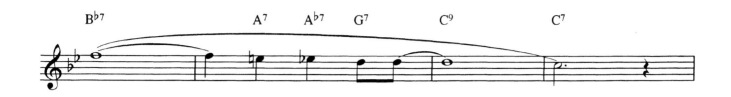

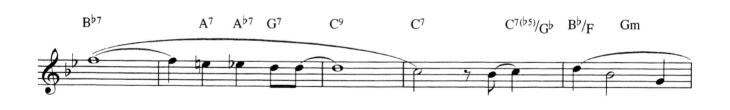

I Remember Clifford

By Benny Golson

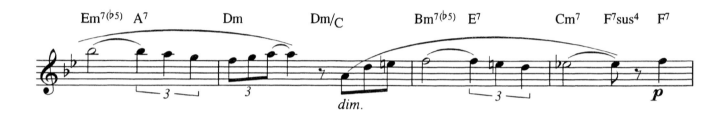

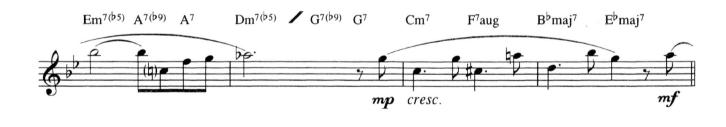

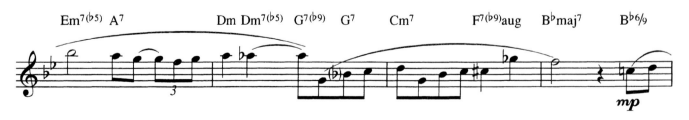

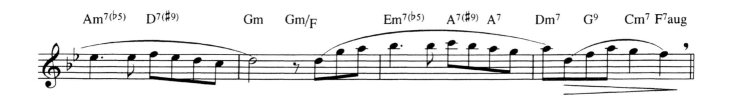

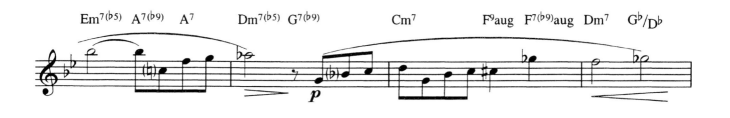

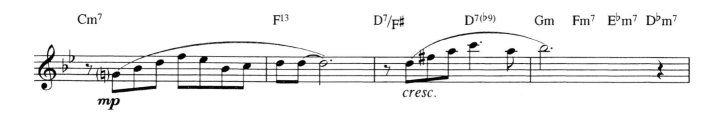

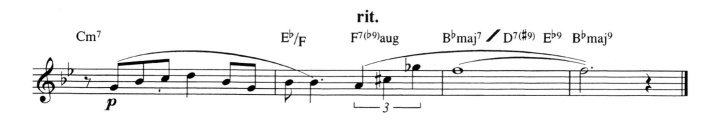

41

I Wanna Be Around

Words & Music by Johnny Mercer & Sadie Vimmerstedt

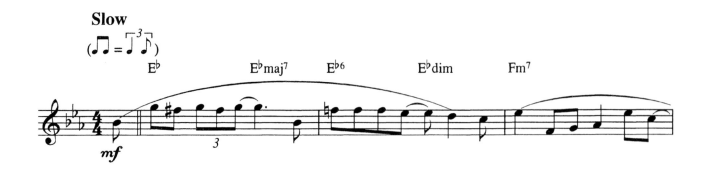

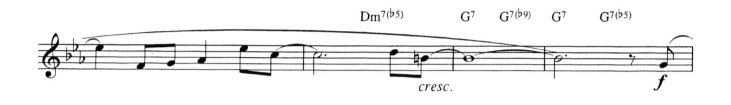

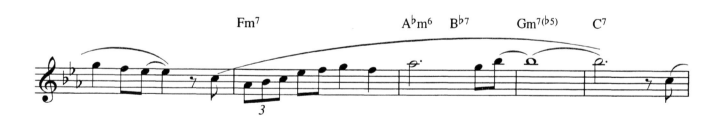

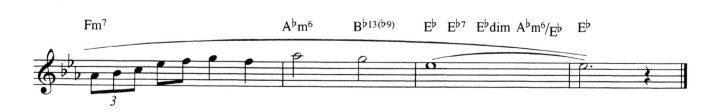

In A Mellow Tone

By Duke Ellington & Milt Gabler

Medium slow

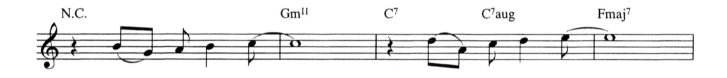

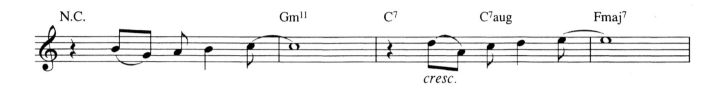

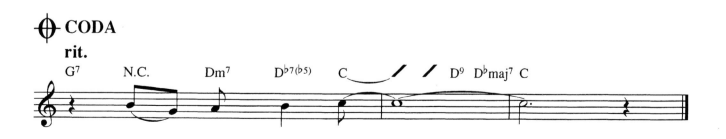

Is You Is, Or Is You Ain't (Ma' Baby)

Words & Music by Billy Austin & Louis Jordan

CODA

47

In The Heat Of The Night

Words by Marilyn & Alan Bergman ▌ Music by Quincy Jones

Slow

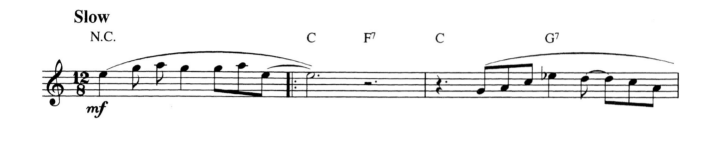

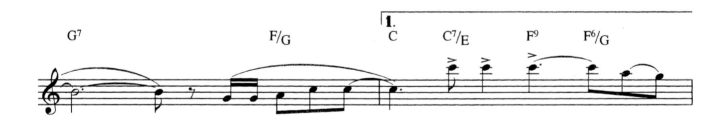

It Could Happen To You

Music by Jimmy Van Heusen ▮ Words by Johnny Burke

Just A Sittin' And A Rockin'

By Duke Ellington

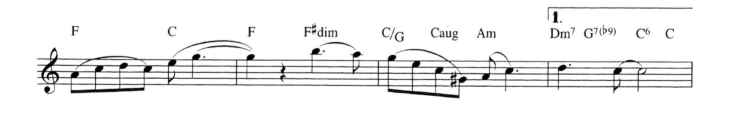

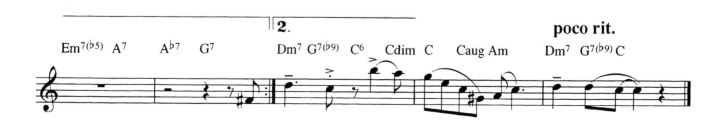

Just Squeeze Me

Words & Music by Duke Ellington & Lee Gaines

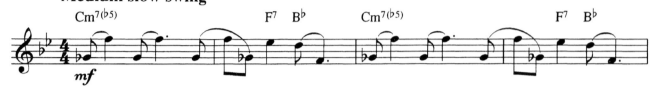

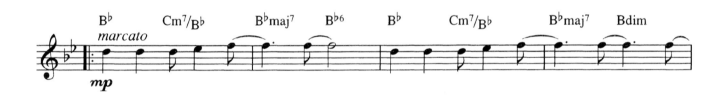

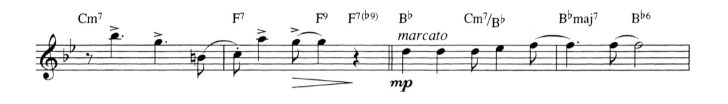

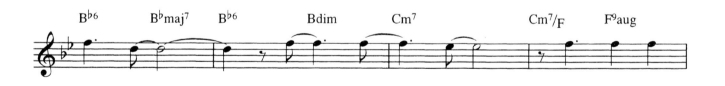

Lean Baby

Words by Roy Alfred ▮ Music by Billy May

Limehouse Blues

Words by Douglas Furber ▮ Music by Phil Braham

Lover Man (Oh Where Can You Be)

Words & Music by Jimmy Davies, Roger Ram Ramirez & Jimmy Sherman

Moonlight Becomes You

Music by Jimmy Van Heusen ▮ Words by Johnny Burke

Mad About Him, Sad Without Him, How Can I Be Glad Without Him Blues

Words & Music by Larry Markes & Dick Charles

Medium swing

D. $ al Coda

CODA

Memphis Blues

Words & Music by W.C. Handy

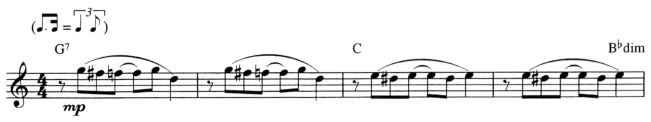

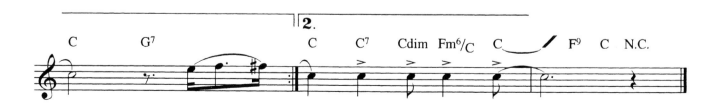

More Than You Know

Words & Music by William Rose & Edward Eliscu ▌ Music by Vincent Youmans

Nine Twenty Special

Words by Bill Engvick ▮ Music by Earl Warren

Medium bounce

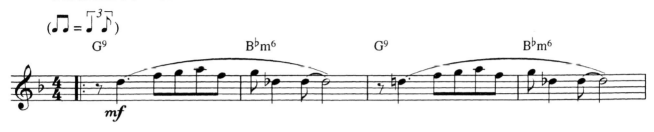

No Smoking

By Duke Ellington

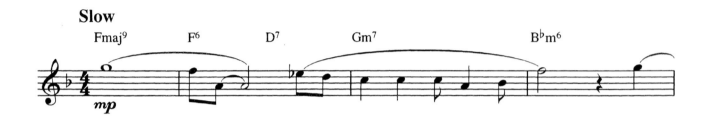

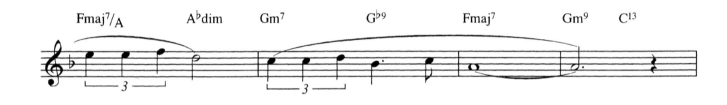

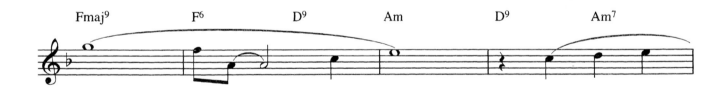

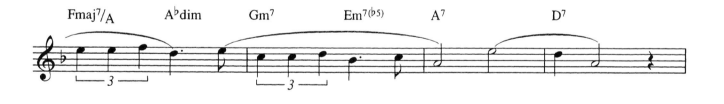

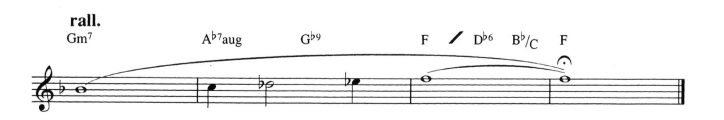

Nobody Knows You When You're Down And Out

Words & Music by Jimmie Cox

Ol' Man Mose

By Louis Armstrong & Zilner Trenton Randolph

On Green Dolphin Street

Words by Ned Washington ❚ Music by Bronislau Kaper

Medium swing

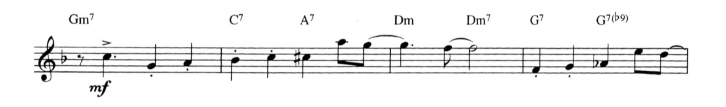

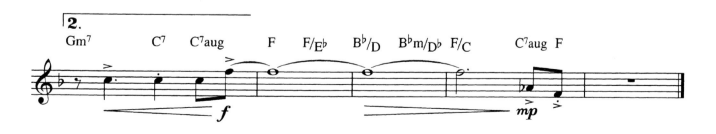

Our Day Will Come

Music by Bob Hilliard ▪ Words by Mort Garson

Prelude To A Kiss

Words & Music by Duke Ellington, Irving Gordon & Irving Mills

Raincheck

By Billy Strayhorn

River Stay 'Way From My Door

Music by Harry Woods ▮ Words by Mort Dixon

Robbin's Nest

By Sir Charles Thompson & Illinois Jacquet

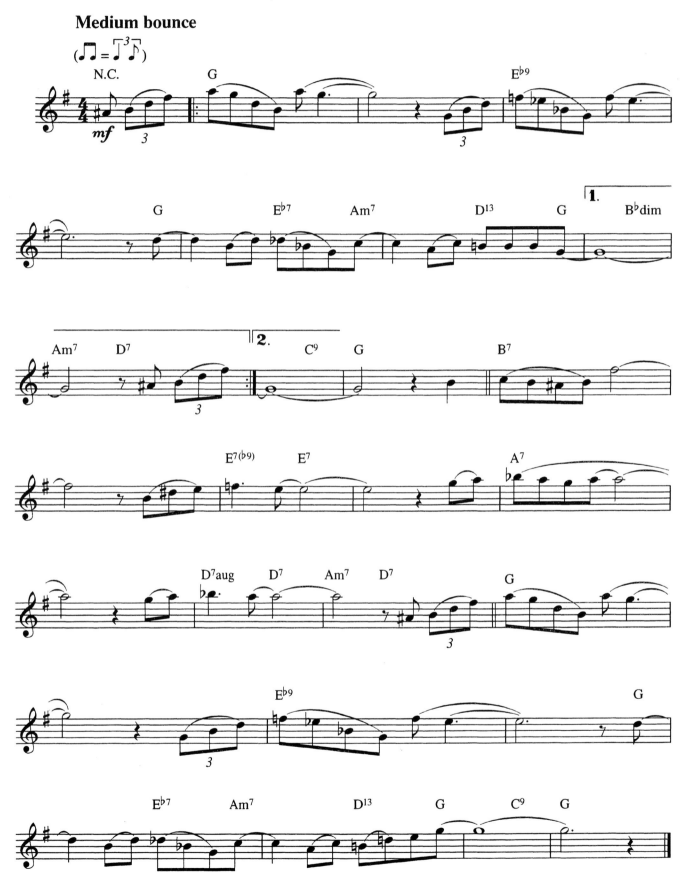

See See Rider

Words & Music by Gertrude 'Ma' Rainey

Solitude

Words by Eddie de Lange & Irving Mills ▪ Music by Duke Ellington

Medium slow

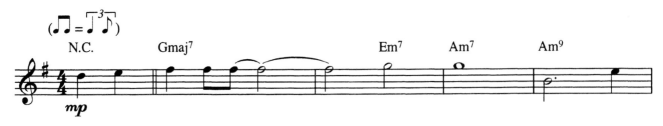

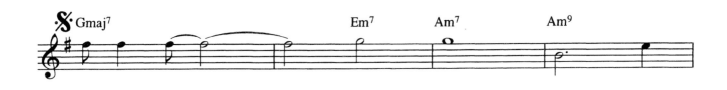

D. $\%$ al Coda

CODA

molto rit.

Someone To Watch Over Me

Music & Lyrics by George Gershwin & Ira Gershwin

St James Infirmary

Words & Music by Joe Primrose

Straight No Chaser

By Thelonious Monk

Sugar Blues

Music by Clarence Williams ▌ Words by Lucy Fletcher

Sultry Serenade

By Duke Ellington

Summertime Blues

Words & Music by Eddie Cochran & Jerry Capehart

Sunny

Words & Music by Bobby Hebb

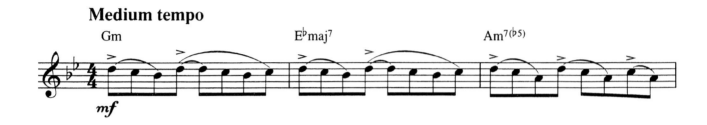

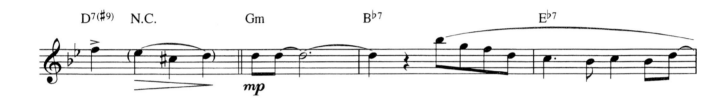

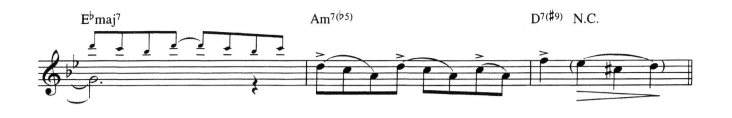

Swingin' Shepherd Blues

Words by Rhoda Roberts & Kenny Jacobson ▮ Music by Moe Koffman

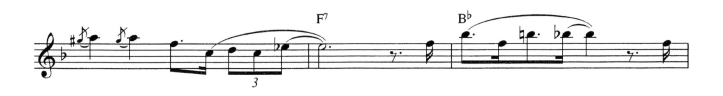

The Birth Of The Blues

Words & Music by Ray Henderson, Lew Brown & Buddy DeSylva

Medium slow

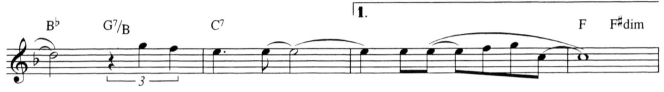

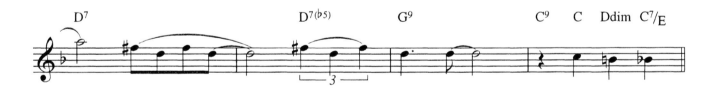

The Lady Sings The Blues

Words by Billie Holiday ■ Music by Herbie Nichols

The Nearness Of You

Music by Hoagy Carmichael ▪ Words by Ned Washington

The Old Piano Roll Blues

Words & Music by Cy Coben

Medium bounce

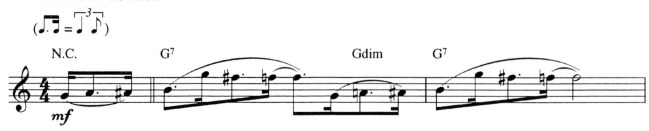

Time's A-Wastin'

Words & Music by Duke Ellington, Mercer Ellington & Don George

When It's Sleepy Time Down South

Words & Music by C. Muse, O. Rene & L. Rene

When Sunny Gets Blue

Words by Jack Segal ▪ Music by Marvin Fisher

When Your Lover Has Gone

Words & Music by E. A. Swan

Willow Weep For Me

Words & Music by Ann Ronell

Yesterdays

Music by Jerome Kern ▪ Words by Otto Harbach

Medium slow

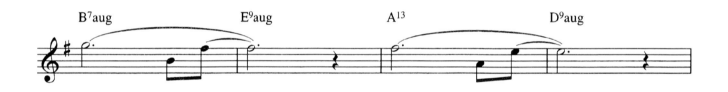

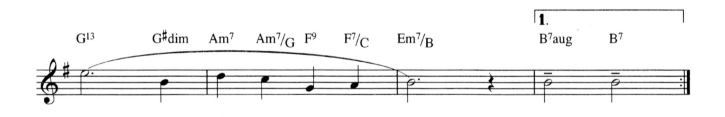

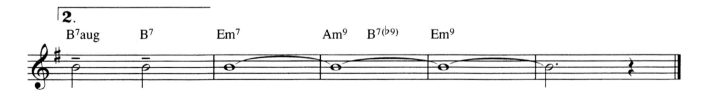

3/04 (50636)